The Gar Gnome Detectives

Written by Emma Spiers

Illustrated by Leo Trinidad

In the daytime, there is nothing unusual about these garden gnomes.

But at night they become ...

The Garden Gnome Detectives!

One night, the garden gnome detectives heard a sound.

They knew that something was wrong.

The gnomes grabbed their backpacks.

These night vision goggles might be useful.

Fetch the magnifying glass.

Here's the measuring tape and a torch. Catch!

The gnomes knew exactly where to search first.

They climbed over the plants to reach the garden gate.

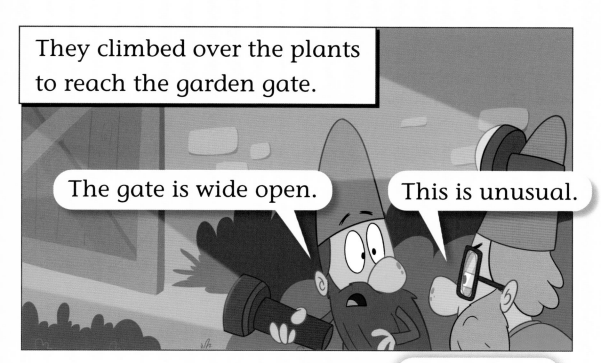

The gate is wide open.

This is unusual.

The latch was broken!

Let me write this down.

The gnomes tiptoed past the kitchen.

The milk bottles have been knocked over.

Shhhhhh …

The gnomes looked closely.

Could it have been the ginger cat from next door?

Suddenly, the gnomes heard an unusual sound.

Smash!

What was that?

A flowerpot had been smashed near the gnomes' pond.

Something is very wrong!

Ribbit! Ribbit!

The gnomes found soil everywhere. They got out the night vision goggles.

They got out their book of paw print facts.

The garden gnome detectives were puzzled.

They scratched their heads and thought hard.

Just then, they heard a clattering noise.

The gnomes knew that they needed to be brave.

The gnomes crept around the corner.

There were stinky ketchup bottles and food wrappers everywhere.

Just then, the gnomes saw another sign that something was wrong. Water was flying everywhere!

Someone has been gnawing at the hosepipe!

This hosepipe is wrecked.

I'm drenched!

The gnomes were just drying off when they spotted something right behind them.

Now, the gnomes were very unhappy.
They liked a tidy lawn!

The gnome detectives measured the holes with their tape.

I don't know what is going on.

They wrote down all the clues they had noticed so far.

This is the strangest case …

Just then, the gnomes heard a noise by the greenhouse.

They were shocked.

Then, things got much worse for the garden gnome detectives.

Someone has been digging up the vegetable patch!

The garden was wrecked.

Carrots, potatoes, radishes, beetroot, leeks – all destroyed!

The gnome friends were beginning to lose hope.

Will we ever catch this intruder?

What shall we do next?

This is a disaster.

The list of clues grew longer and longer.

All of a sudden …

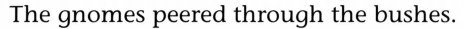

The gnomes peered through the bushes.

The gnomes crept back to their pond.

The case was solved.

Phonics Practice

Say the sound and read the words.

/n/	gn

gnaw   gnash   sign   design   gnome
gnat   resign

/r/	wr

wreck   wrinkle   wriggle   wrong   write
wrap   wring

/ch/	-tch

catch   kitchen   patch   hutch   ditch
match   latch

Can you say your own sentences using some of the words on these pages?

What other words do you know that are spelled in these ways?

/zh/	-s, -si, -ge

usual   measure   treasure   television
beige   collage

Common exception words

looked   called   asked   could   water

We may say some words differently because of our accent.

Talk about the story

Answer the questions:

1 Name four things that the gnomes kept
  in their backpacks.

2 How did the gnomes keep track of all the clues
  they found?

3 What does 'beginning to lose hope' on
  page 17 mean?

4 What made the gnomes realise that the fox was
  the intruder?

5 Do you know any other detective stories like this
  one? What do you like about them?

6 What sounds can you hear at night where you live?

Can you retell the story in your own words?